Standin' Tall
with
GRATITUDE

by
Janeen Brady
Script Co-Authored
by Diane Woolley

Series Includes

Brite

Hi, friends. Today we're going to learn about gratitude. Do you know what gratitude is?

★ **Something you eat?**

No. But listen closely and maybe you can guess.

BADGER: Why, Mr. Bear, how kind of you to stop on your way to work.

BEAR: My pleasure, Mr. Badger.

BADGER: May I share your company as we travel to our place of employment?

BEAR: Why certainly, Mr. Badger. Allow me to open the gate for you.

BADGER: Oh no, allow me.

BEAR: Oh, but I insist.

BADGER: Why, thank you, Mr. Bear.

BEAR: You're most welcome, Mr. Badger.

We're just two friends who like to say thank you,
Out for a stroll.
Two good friends who like to say thank you.
Isn't that droll?
There's a puddle, watch your feet! Thank you kindly.
Would you like a bite to eat? Thanks again.
Let me open up the gate so you won't have to wait,
Thank you, thank you, thank you friend.

We're just two friends who like to say thank you,
Out on a spree.
Two good friends who like to say thank you,
My buddy and me.
I'm so very glad we met. Is there something I could get?
If you please. Thank you, I'm forever in your debt.
Allow me. Allow me. After you. Such courtesy!
Thank, thank, you, you, friend.

★ I like Mr. Badger.

So do I. But let's listen and see what happens.

RABBIT: It's about time you got here.

BEAR: I believe we're three minutes early.

RABBIT: Three minutes early, three minutes late, it's all the same to me.

BADGER: The missus sent some carrots fresh from the garden.

RABBIT: Trying to get on my good side, huh? Well you should have brought better-looking carrots than those if that's what you're trying to do. Get to work, get to work. I don't pay you for standing around. The laundry's sorted and waiting to be washed.

BADGER: Why, thank you, Mr. Rabbit.

RABBIT: "Thank you, Mr. Rabbit; thank you Mr. Rabbit." Auh! It's enough to make a rabbit ill.

BADGER: Only showing a bit of gratitude, sir.

RABBIT: Gratitude, smatitude. Lot of wasted effort if you ask me, all this "thank you" business. If there's one thing I can't stand, it's gratitude. So don't thank me, 'cause I'll never thank you.

I'm only an ingrate in an ingrate world.
Don't they know that I was born to be
An ingrate living in an ingrate world?
I'm completely satisfied with me.
I never say thank you, I never intend.
Nobody likes me, but who needs a friend?
I never say thank you, don't even know how.
And it's too late to change that now.
I'd rather be an ingrate in an ingrate world
Going it entirely alone
Than credit anybody in this ingrate world
With helping me. I'll do it on my own.
No helping me, I'll do it on my own,
On my own, on my own, on my own.

Oh, that silly rabbit. When will he learn that saying "thank you" makes people happy?

★ Is that gratitude, saying thank you?

Partly.

★ Mr. Badger knows about gratitude, but Mr. Rabbit doesn't.

You're right. Let's peek in on Mr. Badger and see if showing gratitude makes him happy.

BADGER: Why Martha, what delicious concoction do you have bubbling on the stove tonight?

MRS. BADGER: Turnip stew, dear, but I'm afraid it's a wee bit overdone.

BADGER: Now, Martha, overdone, underdone, I'm sure it's just the way we like it.

MRS. BADGER: I do love cooking for you, Papa Badger.

Showing gratitude makes others feel good.

BADGER: Bridgette Badger, did you make that bird house yourself?

BRIDGETTE: Yes, Papa, all by myself.

BADGER: And you put away the tools. I'm grateful that you're so careful when you use my things.

BRIDGETTE: Oh, Papa, I forgot to put away the hammer. Next time I'll remember to put every single tool back where it belongs.

Showing gratitude makes others want to try harder.

BADGER: Martha, I believe I see Mr. Skunk out mowing my lawn. Mr. Skunk, you come back here. Don't you try sneaking through those bushes.

SKUNK: I was hoping you wouldn't catch me.

BADGER: Martha, please bring this fine fellow a slice of your gooseberry pie.

SKUNK: You do know how to show gratitude, Mr. Badger.

When we show gratitude others like to do nice things for us.

 When you have a gratitude attitude
Others are going to love you, love you true.
When you have a gratitude attitude
Folks will be happy to do nice things for you.
Having a gratitude attitude shows appreciation.
Those with a gratitude attitude win in every situation.
So please have a gratitude attitude;
Learn to be grateful for all that you enjoy.
When you have a gratitude attitude
You are the happiest kind of girl or boy.

Showing gratitude is very important.

★ **But not everyone understands.**

You're right. Jenny didn't understand. Jenny was a good little girl. She cleaned her room and chewed with her mouth closed and did most of the things good little girls do. But Jenny had a problem: She never said "thank you." When her mother fixed ham and eggs for breakfast, Jenny gobbled it down and said:

★ **How come we don't have this more often?**

When Jenny's big sister drove her to the ball game, Jenny jumped out of the car and said:

★ **Now don't be late coming to pick me up.**

When Jenny's dad drilled her on her spelling words, Jenny said:

★ **That's enough; I have to go now.**

★ **Jenny was ungrateful.**

She certainly was. No matter what people did for her she never said "thank you." If you've done something for someone who forgot to say "thank you," you will know how Jenny's family felt. In fact, they felt so bad they didn't want to do anything nice for her. Suddenly life became very difficult for Jenny.

★ **Dad, can you go over these spelling words with me after my game?**

DAD: Sorry Jenny, but I'm sure I'll be too tired.

★ **Oh, I found my mitt, Sis, let's go.**

SISTER: I don't feel like driving you today, Jenny.

★ **How will I get to my game?**

SISTER: Walk.

★ Walk! Oh, it's so far. What are we having for dinner tonight, Mom?

MOTHER: Nothing, Jenny, I'm not fixing dinner for you.

★ But Mom! Hey everybody, what's going on around here?

DAD: Jenny, when you forget to show gratitude it makes us feel bad, and we don't enjoy doing things for you.

★ But it's your job!

DAD: It's *your* job to say "thank you." When you say "thank you" you're showing us that you know we've done something nice. Think about it, Jenny.

Think about a thank you,
Think about a thank you,
Doesn't hurt a bit to say. It's not much to give away
Two little words.
Think about a thank you,
Think about a thank you,
It won't cost you anything, But it's worth remembering
Two little words.

Sometimes you can write it in a letter.
Sometimes you can sing it in a song.
Sometimes you can say it even better
If you send a gift along.

Think about a thank you,
Think about a thank you,
Let somebody know you care,
Show your gratitude and share
Two little words.
Think about a thank you,
Think about a thank you,
Say it and make someone smile,
They're the most worthwhile
Two little words.

Jenny thought about thank yous, and she decided to start showing gratitude, so . . .

MOTHER: Jenny, come and eat your breakfast.

★ **Ohh, waffles, my favorite! Thanks, Mom.**

MOTHER: Jenny, you said "thanks." I'll have to make waffles more often.

SISTER: Jenny don't you have a game this afternoon?

★ **Yes, and I'm late. I'd sure be grateful if you'd take me.**

SISTER: Jenny, I'll not only take you; I'll stay and cheer for you.

★ **Really? Super!**

DAD: Hey cutie, how did you do on your spelling test?

★ **I got them all right.**

DAD: That's my girl.

★ **Thanks for helping me, Dad. I couldn't have done it without you.**

 When you have a gratitude attitude
Others are going to love you, love you true.
When you have a gratitude attitude
Folks will be happy to do nice things for you.
Having a gratitude attitude shows appreciation.
Those with a gratitude attitude win in every situation.
So please have a gratitude attitude,
Learn to be grateful for all that you enjoy.
When you have a gratitude attitude
You are the happiest kind of girl or boy.
Happiest girl or boy, happiest girl or boy, happiest girl or boy.

Wouldn't it be wonderful if everybody in the world learned to show gratitude?

★ **Even that silly rabbit?**

That's expecting a lot. There's that rabbit now, and it looks as if he's in a bit of trouble.

RABBIT: Now, where am I? I suppose I could have asked somebody for directions back there. No, no, better to work things out for myself. But what am I supposed to do, wander around this frozen forest till I drop from exhaustion? Or get eaten by some mangy beast? I do believe the tips of my ears are freezing, and my stomach, it's never been emptier. Brrr.

★ Is he lost?

I think he is, and the forest is covered with snow. Oh, there's Mr. Squirrel. Now he's a friendly chap, and Mr. Rabbit could use a friend. Let's watch and see what happens.

SQUIRREL: I say there, Mr. Rabbit, sir, you look a bit frozen around the edges. Could you do with a spot of warm milk?

RABBIT: I won't give help, and I won't ask for any. *Thank yous* are something I can't abide. Now leave me alone. Brrr, it's freezing.

SQUIRREL: The poor fellow's nearly all in. I'll follow along for a bit and see if I can help.

★ Why is Mr. Rabbit lying down?

He's too cold to walk any farther.

SQUIRREL: He's quite frozen, I'm afraid. Okay, crew, careful now. We don't want to awaken the old codger when we hoist him up, but he'll never survive in this cold. All together now—one, two, three, pull! Careful, watch out for that ear. Pull. We did it; he's safe in our warm tree.

RABBIT: Humph, what's this? Warm milk, mmmm. My ears, what's on my ears?

BABY SQUIRREL: We wrapped them in newspaper, sir, to warm them up.

RABBIT: Well, of all the . . .

SQUIRREL: Before you carry on, sir, you were about to meet your untimely demise. So, even being the ingrate you are, my crew and I brought you up our tree to . . .

RABBIT: Up a tree? I'm up a tree!

SQUIRREL: Just long enough to warm you some. Then we'll give you directions to get home. Drink your milk.

BABY SQUIRREL: Look, his toes are starting to wiggle, and his ears are turning pink again.

RABBIT: Oh, what is this I'm starting to feel in my cold, ungrateful heart? I've never felt this before. Could it . . . could it be?

★ Is he feeling gratitude?

I believe he is.

RABBIT: Well, it feels absolutely wonderful!

SQUIRREL: Give the fellow some room, crew, give him some room.

RABBIT: Suddenly I'm beginning to feel an uncontrollable urge to say . . . no, I couldn't, I just couldn't. But I can't help myself. Oh, dear. Here it comes—Oh . . . um . . . ah . . . thank you. Why, that didn't hurt at all! In fact, it felt rather good. Thank you. I say thank you! Thank you, thank you, thank you, thank you, thank you, thank you, thank you, thank you.

 Thank you, I say thank you.
Though I never really planned for you to help me, you've been grand,
And I say thank you.
Thank you, I say thank you.
Though I thought I could succeed I needed help, I did indeed,
And I say thank you.

Thank you, I say thank you.
When I shuddered with despair and I felt no one would care,
You were there, thank you.
Thank you, I say thank you.
When I quite mistakenly thought I needed only me it wasn't true;
I needed you.

Thank you, I say thank you.
I have learned my lesson well and I shall very gladly tell
Somebody thank you.
Thank you, I say thank you.
And I promise ever more to be more grateful than before,
And I'll say thank you.

RABBIT: Thank you, thank you, thank you.

We all need each other. Sometimes it's our turn to help others, and sometimes it's their turn to help us. And it's always someone's turn to say thank you.

★ **That's right.**

Why don't we dance a "thank you" dance.

★ **May I be your partner?**

Yes you may.

★ **That sounds fun.**

 There is a beautiful dance called the Thank You.
I hear it playing now.
Won't everyone do the dance called the Thank You?
Come, I will teach you how.

Let's dance the Thank You Dance—
Glide, glide, and turn around.
Sway to the Thank You Dance
Slide, slide and turn around.
Smile as you sway and dance
One more time around.
Now step back gracefully
Then curtsey with me and say
Thank you. Thank you, thank you.

Side A of each cassette contains the complete program. **Side B** repeats the same program but leaves out the lines of the main child in the story, giving the listener the chance to read along, saying aloud the missing lines and actually becoming a member of the cast. This fascinating activity helps older children with their reading and provides an excellent opportunity for development in dramatics.

Children can sing along with the songs, color the pictures and participate in still other activities as the story progresses.

A Product of BRITE MUSIC ENTERPRISES, INC.
Music recorded and engineered at Skaggs Telecommunications Service, Inc.
Dramatics and final mix by Bonneville Productions.
Illustrations by Grant Wilson / Graphic production by Whipple & Associates.
Music arranged, conducted and mixed by Merrill Jenson.